The Strictly Dancing Piano Book

Written and arranged by Sarah Walker

FABER _ff_ MUSIC

Contents

© 2009 by Faber Music Ltd
This edition first published in 2009
Bloomsbury House 74–77 Great Russell Street London WC1B 3DA
Music processed by Jeanne Roberts
Cover and text designed by Susan Clarke
Illustrations by Andy Cooke
Printed in England by Caligraving Ltd
All rights reserved

ISBN10: 0-571-53299-3
EAN13: 978-0-571-53299-5

To buy Faber Music publications or to find out about the full
range of titles available please contact your local music retailer
or Faber Music sales enquiries:
Faber Music Ltd, Burnt Mill, Elizabeth Way, Harlow CM20 2HX
Tel: +44 (0) 1279 82 89 82   Fax: +44 (0) 1279 82 89 83
sales@fabermusic.com   fabermusic.com

Waltz of the Snowflakes

In Tchaikovsky's ballet *The Nutcracker*, Clara is whisked off to a magical kingdom by a nutcracker that turns into a prince. She finds herself in the Land of Snow, where she is welcomed by dancing snowflakes.

8/1/13

Pyotr Ilyich Tchaikovsky

3

Funky Cha-cha

The cha-cha (or cha-cha-cha) is a Latin-American dance based on Cuban rhythms. In today's ballrooms it's usually energetic with a steady beat.

Sarah Walker

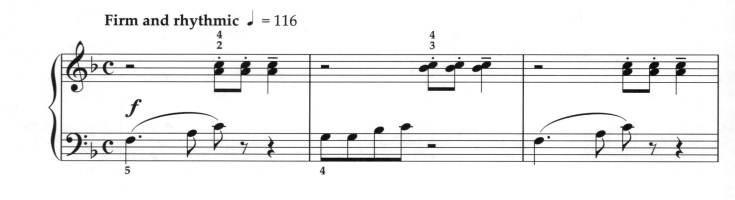

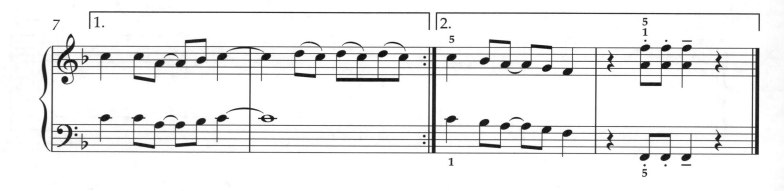

Teacher's accompaniment

Cheek to Cheek

This famous song is by the American composer Irving Berlin. You may know the first line: 'Heaven, I'm in heaven, and my heart beats so that I can hardly speak …' Fred Astaire performed it in the 1935 movie *Top Hat*.

Words and music by Irving Berlin

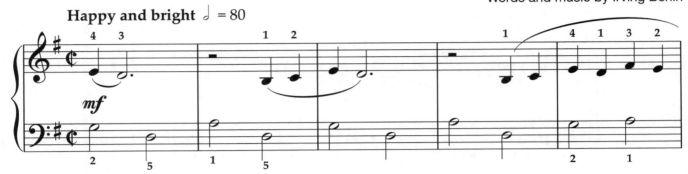

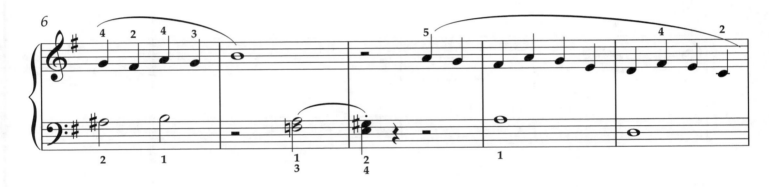

Teacher's accompaniment

Cross-patch Tango

The tango is a passionate dance from South America, and is especially
associated with the capital city of Argentina, Buenos Aires. It's also a
popular ballroom dance throughout the world.

Sarah Walker

Teacher's accompaniment

Like an accordion (you could use the accordion voice on an electronic keyboard)

Jivin' Easy

Jive dancing comes from America in the early 1940s. It's lively and usually performed to jazzy music. This jive uses the same five-finger position in different areas of the keyboard.

Sarah Walker

Teacher's accompaniment

Blues from 'An American in Paris'

George Gershwin wrote *An American in Paris* in 1928. Later it inspired a famous film starring Gene Kelly and Leslie Caron, who danced a sultry blues to this theme.

Music by George Gershwin

Millie is helping out at a dance shop, but she's getting all the different types of shoes rather muddled up!

Can you help her? Draw an arrow between the shoes and their name.

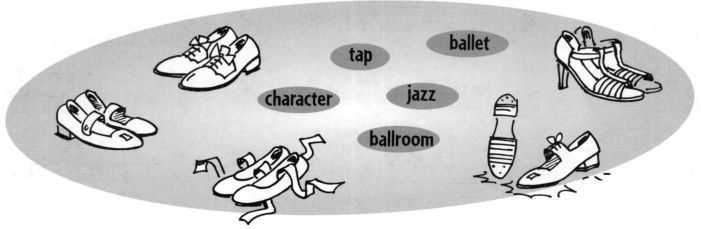

tap   ballet   character   jazz   ballroom

Memory of a Waltz

This nostalgic waltz has a folk-like flavour.
Each hand stays in the same five-finger position.

Sarah Walker

Teacher's accompaniment

Two Left Feet

Sarah Walker

Passionate Paso Doble

Sarah Walker

Yellow Bird Rumba

Yellow bird, up high in banana tree,
Yellow bird, you sit all alone like me.
Did your ladyfriend leave the nest again? That is very sad, makes me feel so bad.
You can fly away in the sky away, you're more lucky than me.

Light rhumba ♩ = 138

Traditional Jamaican

Teacher's accompaniment

You could try this using the flute voice on an electronic keyboard.

Miss Suki Mambo, Dame Gertrude Poynt and Sir Henry Fox-Trotter are three of the nation's leading dance judges. But they've lost their score boards, so we can't tell who's been generous, who's been mean, and who's hedging their bets! Can you lead each judge back to their board?

Let's Face the Music and Dance

This song by Irving Berlin is used in a celebrated dance duet with Fred Astaire and Ginger Rogers. The words start: 'There may be trouble ahead; but while there is music and moonlight and love and romance… let's face the music and dance.'

Words and music by Irving Berlin

Teacher's accompaniment

Expressively ♩ = 92

Play an octave lower throughout

Unscramble the names of these Hollywood stars, famed for their great dancing:

LELK GENEY

CLUE He starred in the films 'An American in Paris' and 'Singing in the Rain'.

RINGS GREEGOR

CLUE She could do anything Fred Astaire could, only backwards and in high heels!

DEAF RASTRIE

CLUE Perhaps the most celebrated Hollywood dancer of all.

TROL THANAJOV

CLUE Star of a 1970's disco spectacular film.

Line Dance Bonanza

This is a country-and-western style piece, inspired by line dancing.

Sarah Walker

Teacher's accompaniment Like a bluegrass fiddle

Fred and Ginger's Foxtrot

Fred Astaire and Ginger Rogers were two of the most famous dancers of the 20th century. This foxtrot mixes ragtime, Charleston and swing to conjure up a dance from the early years of cinema.

Sarah Walker

Teacher's accompaniment

Disco Ball Fever

Have you ever seen a glittering mirror ball, hanging above a dance floor?
This piece conjures up the fun and excitement of a 1970's disco, with wild
fashions and platform shoes all illuminated by the twinkling of the ball.

Joyful and rhythmic, not too heavy ♩ = 104

Sarah Walker

Teacher's accompaniment

Joyful and rhythmic, not too heavy ♩ = 104

Colour in these dance costumes

Bop to the Top from 'High School Musical'

In Disney's *High School Musical,* Sharpay and her brother Ryan do a wild Latin dance
to this tune, hoping to upstage Gabriella and Troy. But their plans don't quite work out …

Words and Music by Kevin Quinn
and Randy Petersen

Teacher's accompaniment

Very lively, with a salsa feel ♩ = 96

Find these words
hidden in the grid:

MAMBO

SAMBA

TANGO

PIROUETTE

ARABESQUE

BEGUINE

BALLET

FOXTROT

KICK

JIVE

SHIMMY

BOOGIE

Wordsearch

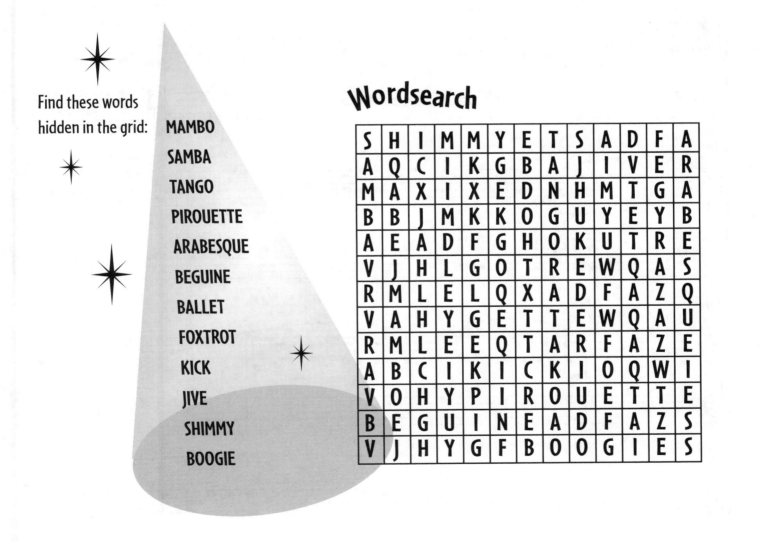

Dancing Queen

Words and Music by Stig Anderson,
Benny Andersson and Björn Ulvaeus

Teacher's accompaniment

Answers

page 8

Ballroom =

Tap =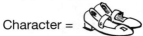

Ballet =

Jazz =

Character =

page 13

 Miss Suki Mambo
gave 7 points

Dame Gertrude Poynt
gave 3 points

 Sir Henry Fox-Trotter
gave 10 points

page 15

Gene Kelly
Ginger Rogers
Fred Astaire
John Travolta

page 21

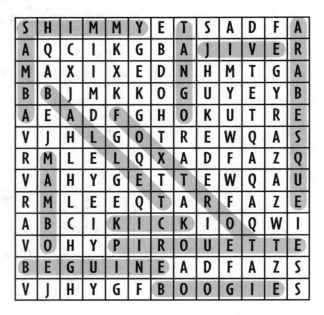

Exclusive distributors:
Music Sales Limited, 8/9 Frith Street,
London W1D 3JB, England.

Music Sales Pty Limited, 120 Rothschild Avenue, Rosebery,
NSW 2018, Australia.

Order No.AM969254 ISBN 0-7119-8708-4
This book © Copyright 2000 by Wise Publications.

Music arranged by Roger Day. Music engraved by Paul Ewers Music Design.

Printed in the United Kingdom by Printwise Limited, Haverhill, Suffolk.

Your Guarantee of Quality: As publishers, we strive to produce every book to the highest commercial standards.
The music has been freshly engraved and, whilst endeavouring to retain the original running order of the recorded
album, the book has been carefully designed to minimise awkward page turns and to make playing from it a real
pleasure. Particular care has been given to specifying acid-free, neutral-sized paper made from pulps which
have not been elemental chlorine bleached. This pulp is from farmed sustainable forests and was produced
with special regard for the environment. Throughout, the printing and binding have been planned to ensure
a sturdy, attractive publication which should give years of enjoyment. If your copy fails to meet our high
standards, please inform us and we will gladly replace it.

Music Sales' complete catalogue describes thousands of titles and is available in full colour
sections by subject, direct from Music Sales Limited. Please state your areas of
interest and send a cheque/postal order for £1.50 for postage to: Music Sales
Limited, Newmarket Road, Bury St. Edmunds, Suffolk IP33 3YB.

www.musicsales.com

I need the near - ness of you to get by.————————

Ba - by I just want -ed you to know that if you can, you could be part of my—— life,——

ba - by don't you know we could be do - ing this for - ev - er and be do - ing al - right.——

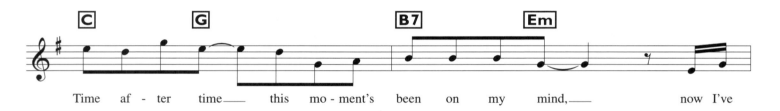

Time af - ter time—— this mo - ment's been on my mind,—— now I've

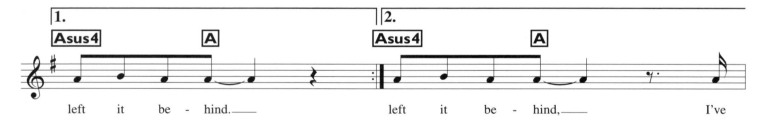

1.
left it be - hind.——

2.
left it be - hind,—— I've

left it be - hind,———— don't get me wrong.——

Verse 2:
Don't get me wrong, you bruised my heart and it's aching.
It won't take you long to see that I'm in pain.
Don't get me wrong, if you run off now you'll sure be mistaken
This love's for real, and baby this is how I feel.

Time after time I've been trying to deny
I can't go on without you by my side.

to see why, I can't go on with-out you by my side.

Ba - by I just want-ed you to know that if you can, you could be part of my life,

ba - by don't you know we could be do - ing this for - ev - er and be do - ing al - right.

Time af - ter time this mo-ment's been on my mind, now I've left it be - hind. Oh,

don't get me wrong.

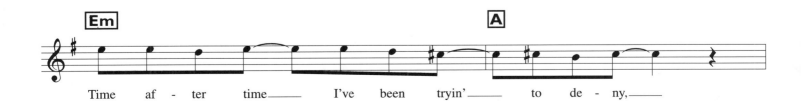

Don't get me wrong, no no ba - by.

Time af - ter time I've been tryin' to de - ny,

24/5/02

DON'T GET ME WRONG

Words & Music by Jake & Anders Von Hofsten

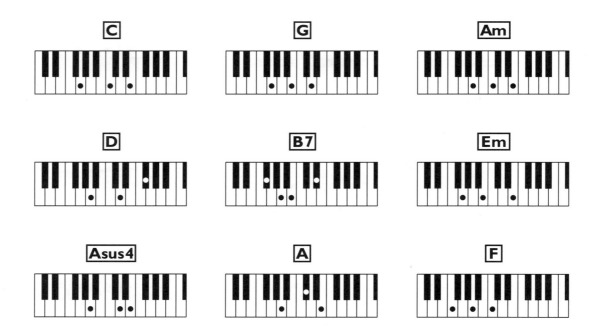

16 beat

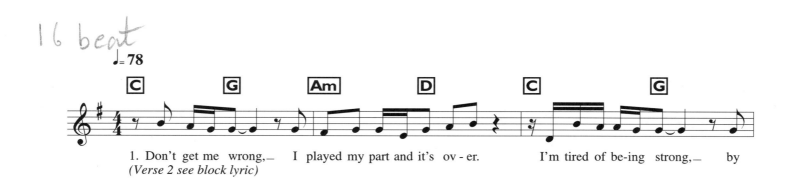

1. Don't get me wrong,— I played my part and it's ov - er.   I'm tired of be-ing strong,— by
(Verse 2 see block lyric)

hid - ing that I'm not,— yeah.— Don't get me wrong,— you've played your part and I think you know—

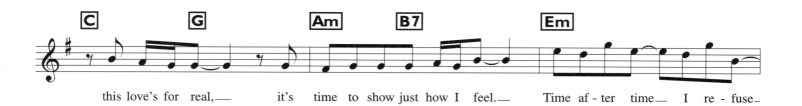

this love's for real,— it's time to show just how I feel.— Time af - ter time— I re - fuse—